Jesus
the Teacher

Leena Lane - Gillian Chapman

The wise and foolish builders

Something to think about:
How can we listen to Jesus?

Jesus once said:

'Anyone who listens to my words and does what I say is like a wise man who built his house upon a rock. The rain poured down, the wind blew hard, the rivers rose and tried to wash the house away. But the house didn't budge.

'But if you don't listen to what I say, you are like a foolish man who built his house upon the sand. The rain poured down, the wind blew hard, the rivers rose and tried to wash the house away. And the house fell down with an enormous CRASH!'

Luke 6, verses 47 to 49

✎ Activity:

What two things do you need to do to be like the wise man?

✎ Activity:

Can you spot all ten differences between the pictures?

Prayer:

Dear God, help me to understand how to do the right things and live in a way that pleases you.

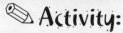

The hidden treasure

Jesus told another story about a man who found some treasure.

'Once a man found treasure hidden in a field. It was beautiful! It sparkled in the sunlight so that the man wanted to keep it. He covered it with earth again so that it was hidden in the ground.

'Then the man went away and sold everything that he had in the world, including his clothes, so that he could have enough money to buy the field. And by buying the field, he had also bought the treasure. Now the treasure belonged to him! He was really happy!'

Matthew 13, verse 44

 **Activity:**
What kind of jewels are coloured like this?

Something to think about:
What is your greatest treasure?

✐Activity:

Connect the dots in the direction of the black lines to complete the picture.

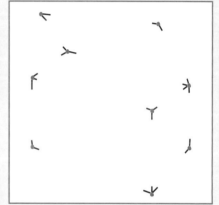

Prayer:

Dear God, help me to know that you are more important than anything else in the world.

The good Samaritan

Jesus told this story to a man who asked how he could serve God best.

'One day, a man was travelling from Jerusalem to Jericho. Suddenly, a gang of robbers jumped out from behind a rock. They took all his money and clothes and hurt him badly.

'The poor man lay in the road, unable to get up. Who could help him now?

'He heard the sound of footsteps. It was a priest. But the priest walked on by.

'Later on, a temple helper walked past, but he didn't stop either!

'The poor man in the road thought that now he really would die. But suddenly he heard more footsteps. It was a man from Samaria. He spoke kindly to the injured man, nursed his wounds, helped him on to his donkey and took him to an inn. He gave silver coins to the innkeeper to look after him.'

Jesus asked, 'Who acted as a neighbour to the injured man?'

'The one who helped him,' replied the man.

'Go and do the same,' said Jesus.

Luke 10, verses 30 to 37

Something to think about:
Are you a good friend to the people around you?

Activity:
Can you find your way through the maze to help the injured man?

Activity:
The man was on his way from where and where was he going?

J _ _ _ _ _ _ _ _ _

TO

_ _ _ _ _ _ _ _ O

6

Prayer:
Dear God, please help me to think of others and how I can help them.

A very greedy man

 Jesus taught that it was not good to be greedy.

'There was once a man who was very rich. He was a farmer, so at first he stored all his crops in barns. When they became too full, he thought he would simply build bigger barns and enjoy all he had.

'He said to himself, "Now I've stored up good things for many years. I'll eat, drink and take life easy."

'But God spoke to him: "You fool! Tonight your life will be taken from you. What good will all your riches be to you then?"'

Jesus said, 'This is how it will be for people who keep all they have for themselves but do not think about God or other people.'

Luke 12, verses 16 to 21

Something to think about:

What do you give to God?

✏️ Activity:

There are eleven coins hidden in the picture. Can you find eleven more coins hidden on these two pages?

Activity:
Can you find the eleven coins hidden in the picture?

Prayer:
Dear God, help me not to be greedy, but to share what I have with others.

Activity:
How many coins are there all together?

Do not worry

Jesus told his disciples not to worry about food or clothes.

'Do not worry about your life,' he said. 'Life is more important than food, and the body is more important than clothes. Look at the ravens – God feeds them all. You are much more important than the birds. And look at the flowers of the field. They are more beautiful than a King's clothes! If that is how God clothes the flowers of the field, how much more will he look after you?

'Try to see how God wants you to live first, and God will give you everything you need.'

Luke 12, verses 22 to 34

✎ Activity:
What do these creatures eat?

Something to think about:
What sort of things do you worry about easily?

10

Activity:

Can you find ten things in the word search that people worry about?

Prayer:
Dear God, thank you that you always look after me. Help me to trust you for everything I need.

```
Q S P I D E R S F R E T U
J O C O F J I R R S B S N
G M L S O E F Y I N C C D
H G O E O A E H E A L T H
O O T P D S D P N K I E R
S C H O O L L P D E F S E
T G E N E T O Y S S E W N
S O S Y J O B S A R O O A
```

The lost sheep

Jesus told a story about a shepherd who had a hundred sheep.

'The shepherd looked after each of his sheep. He made sure they had enough grass and fresh water and protected them from wild animals.

'One day the shepherd found that one was missing. So he set out to find his lost sheep, leaving the ninety-nine other sheep in the sheepfold.

'He looked high and low, behind bushes and rocks. Where could the sheep be?

'After some time, the shepherd heard faint bleating; it was the lost sheep! He picked it up lovingly and carried it home on his shoulders. He was so pleased to have found his lost sheep that he invited all his neighbours to a party.

'God is like that shepherd,' said Jesus. 'He cares even if only one of his sheep is lost.'

Luke 15, verses 4 to 7

Something to think about:

Have you ever lost and found something very important to you?

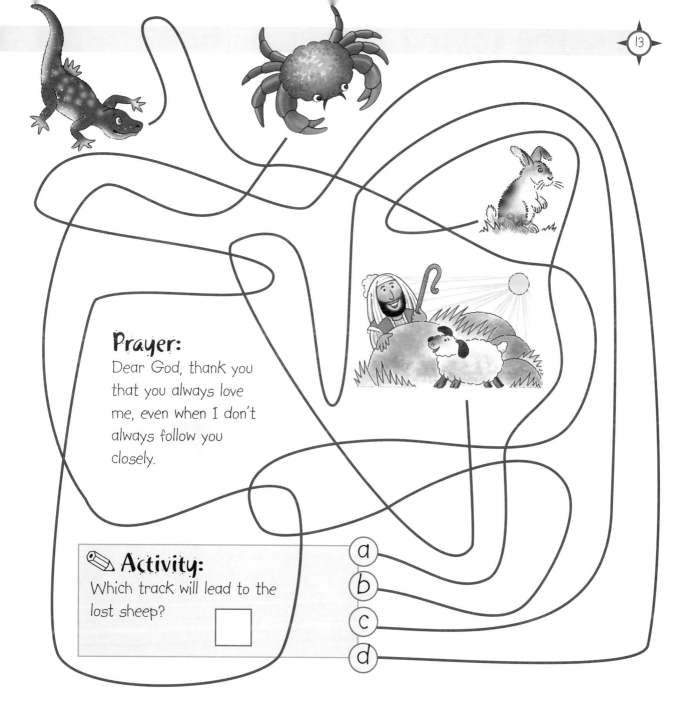

Prayer:
Dear God, thank you that you always love me, even when I don't always follow you closely.

✎ **Activity:**
Which track will lead to the lost sheep?

a
b
c
d

The loving father

There was a young man who lived on a farm with his family. He grew bored and wanted to go to the big city. So he asked his dad for his share of his riches, and set off.

His father was very sad. He loved his son very much and hoped he would return.

The son spent all the money very quickly. But when the money ran out, nobody wanted to be his friend.

He had to find a job, feeding pigs. He was so hungry, he nearly ate the pigs' food. 'I must go home,' he thought. 'Perhaps Dad will let me work on his farm.'

As he came near to his old home, he saw his dad running towards him, shouting: 'Welcome home!' The father gave a great party for his son. He thought he had lost him, but the son he loved had come back. How happy that made him!'

Luke 15, verses 11 to 32

Activity: Join the dots in the direction of the red lines to complete the picture.

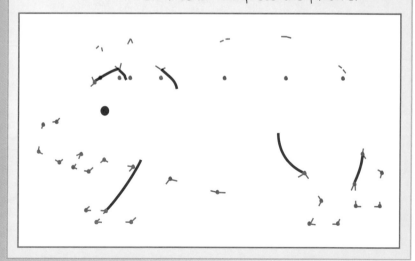

Don't forget to add a wiggly tail.

Something to think about:

God forgives everyone who says sorry and turns back to him.

✎ Activity:

What did the father shout as his son returned?

Prayer:

Dear God, I'm sorry for things I've done wrong today. I'm sorry that...

✎ Activity:

Can you count the pigs in the picture above?

Two men at the temple

Jesus told this story to people who thought they were better than everyone else. 'One day two men went to the temple to pray to God.

'One man thought he was very good and prayed, "Dear God, thank you that I am not greedy or a liar like other people. Thank you that I am not like that poor man over there. I pray to you at all the right times and give you just the right amount of my money."

'The other man was not so pleased with himself. He prayed, "Dear God,

I'm really sorry for all the things I've done wrong. Please forgive me."

'The two men went home. God was pleased with the second man, not the first.'

Luke 18, verses 9 to 14

Something to think about:

Why was God pleased with the second man?

Prayer:

Dear God, I'm sorry for the wrong things I do. Help me not to be proud or big-headed.

✎ Activity:

Here are nine details taken from the big picture. Some copies are right, some have mistakes. Place the word 'right' under the correct copies and the word 'wrong' under the others.

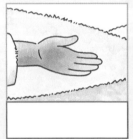

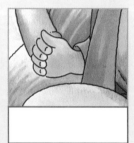

The rich young ruler

A rich young ruler asked Jesus, 'What must I do to have eternal life?'

'Keep the ten commandments,' said Jesus.

'I've kept them all my life,' said the young man.

'Then there is one more thing,' said Jesus. 'Sell everything you have and give it all to the poor. Then come, follow me.'

The young man was very sad, because he was very rich.

Jesus said, 'It is very hard for rich people to enter God's kingdom. It is easier for a camel to go through the eye of a needle.'

Luke 18, verses 18 to 30

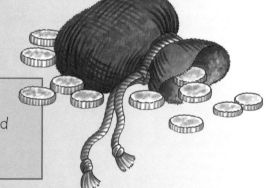

Something to think about:
If you were very rich, do you think you would find it hard to give all your money away?

Activity:
Can you colour in the picture?

Activity:
The opposite of rich is poor. What is the opposite of the following?

Young

Sad

Easy

Prayer:
Dear God, help me to follow you first and not be greedy for fine things or money.

The widow's two coins

Jesus was in the temple in Jerusalem, watching people putting money into the collecting box. The money was an offering to God.

Some rich people were giving a lot of money. Everyone stopped and watched. The rich people felt very pleased with themselves.

Then a very poor widow shuffled towards the collecting box. She didn't want anyone to notice her. She only had two very small coins to give to God.

'Clink!' the two small coins dropped quietly into the box.

The widow moved quietly away. Jesus told his friends to come closer to him.

'That poor widow has just given more than anyone else,' said Jesus. 'Everyone else gave what they didn't really need. But this widow gave everything she has to God.'

Luke 21, verses 1 to 4

Something to think about:
Who gave more generously, the rich who gave a lot, or the poor woman who gave two coins?

✎ Activity:

Which of these is the same rich man as pictured on the opposite page?

Prayer:

Dear God, thank you for all you give to me. Help me to give you everything.

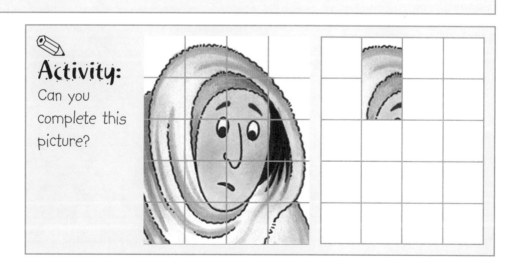

✎ Activity:

Can you complete this picture?

Living God's way

Jesus once spoke about the time he would come back to earth as King. 'The King will say to one group of people: "The Kingdom of heaven is ready for you. When I was hungry, you gave me food. When I was thirsty, you gave me a drink. You didn't know me, but your family welcomed me. You gave me clothes to wear. When I was ill, you looked after me. When I was in prison, you came to visit."

'"When did we do that?" asked the people.

'"When you did these things for anyone who needed help," said the King, "you did it for me."'

Matthew 25, verses 31 to 45

 **Activity:**

Draw an arrow from each circular detail to the same detail in the big picture.

Prayer:

Dear God, help me to notice when other people need help, and be kind to them, whoever they are.

Something to think about:

Why should we be kind to others?

 **Activity:**

Draw an arrow to link each *blue* box to the right pink box.

When I was thirsty...	you gave me food.
When I was a prisoner...	you welcomed me.
When I was a stranger...	you gave me a drink.
When I was ill...	you visited me.
When I was hungry...	you gave me clothes to wear.
When I was cold...	you looked after me.

 **Activity:**

What would you do to help?

When I was sad...	→
When I was lost...	→

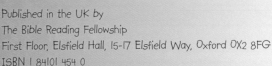

Published in the UK by
The Bible Reading Fellowship
First Floor, Elsfield Hall, 15-17 Elsfield Way, Oxford OX2 8FG
ISBN 1 84101 454 0

First edition 2005

Copyright © 2005 AD Publishing Services Ltd
1 Churchgates, The Wilderness, Berkhamsted, Herts HP4 2UB
Text copyright © 2005 AD Publishing Services Ltd, Leena Lane
Illustrations copyright © 2005 Gillian Chapman

Editorial Director Annette Reynolds
Art Director Gerald Rogers
Pre-production Krystyna Hewitt
Production John Laister

British Library Cataloguing in Publication Data.
A catalogue record for this book is available from the British Library.

Printed and bound in Singapore